M000318325

Why You're Gonna Do Great

When it comes to

_____ ,

you always nail it.

People really seem to admire your

_____.

Obviously, you were born to

_____

great

_____.

Only you can get away with

_____.

Watching you

———————————————————————

is inspiring.

When they coined the phrase

"_____",

they must've been talking about you.

I'd bet money on you getting that

_____

you want.

You make a terrific

_____ .

Your ability to

_____

should be studied by science.

10

It's great how you

_____

every day.

You are the greatest

_____

in our

_____ .

12

When you decide to

_____

people are gonna

_____

it.

You've got great taste in

_____ .

14

If you were a superhero, you'd be

_____.

Got to admit I'm kind of jealous of your

_____ .

16

It's great how you're usually
right about

_____ .

You make

_____

look easy.

I'm sure you could convince

_____

to

_____

if you tried.

19

I'd be honored to

_____

with you someday.

Even when you're

———————————————————— ,

you're still pretty great.

I've learned a lot about

_____

from you.

You've got a real talent for

_____ .

I'm still impressed by how
great you were when we

_____ .

24

If we could bottle and sell your

—————————————————————,

we'd both be filthy rich.

Your knack for

_____

would make anyone envious.

26

You have a way of making people feel

_____ .

27

I love to brag about what a great

_____

you are.

Being your

_____

makes me look really good.

You should be so proud about how you

_____

that time.

30

If aliens invaded, you'd be the first person they ask for

_____

advice.

31

It's great how you always

_____ .

It's great how you never

_____.

If you were a rock 'n' roll anthem,
you'd be

_____ .

34

Remember that time you totally aced that

_____?

Yeah, me too.

I'd like to toast you with a

_____.

Someone needs to

_____

a

_____

about you.

37

You win the

_____

Award.

38

I wish more people were as

_____

as you are.

Bet you were great at

_____

when you were a kid.

Your nickname should be

_____ .

I really respect your

_____.

If

_____

didn't already exist, you probably
would've invented it.

43

I've noticed that when you

_____

you always seem to

_____.

It's great that you've already

_____ .

You could seriously start a

_____ .

Your dedication to

_____

is remarkable.

47

Nobody else can

---

like you.

48

You

_____

the greatest

_____

ever.

49

You make me want to be a better

_____ .

I'm so lucky to be your

_____ .

You're gonna
do great!

Fill in the *Love*.®

Created, published, and distributed by Knock Knock
1635-B Electric Ave.
Venice, CA 90291
knockknockstuff.com
Knock Knock is a registered trademark of Knock Knock LLC
Fill in the Love is a registered trademark of Knock Knock LLC

ISBN: 978-160106923-8
UPC: 825703-50253-4

10 9 8 7 6 5 4 3 2 1